The Call
of the Wild

Based on the Novel by Jack London
Adapted by Sean McCollum

SCHOLASTIC INC.

New York   Toronto   London   Auckland   Sydney
Mexico City   New Delhi   Hong Kong   Buenos Aires

**Illustrations
Kris Wiltse**

Developed by ONO Books in cooperation with Scholastic Inc.

Text copyright © 2003 by Scholastic Inc.
Illustrations copyright © 2003 by Kris Wiltse.
All rights reserved. Published by Scholastic Inc.
Printed in the U.S.A.

ISBN 0-439-59783-8

17 16 15 14 13   23   12 11

Contents

Welcome to This Book

Have you ever had a pet? If your pet could talk, what would it say? Would it be happy to stay in a warm, safe home with plenty of food? Or do you think it longs to be free?

In this book, Buck the dog tells his own story. He begins life as a favorite pet on a big farm. But then everything changes. He is stolen and beaten. Then he's taken to the wilds of Alaska. There, he's nearly worked to death and has to fight for his life. Buck is changing. He's no longer anyone's pet.

Will he answer the call of the wild?

Target Words Buck's new life in Alaska is nothing like his old life. These words will help you understand the difference.

- **instinct:** a gut feeling about what to do in order to survive

  When another dog attacks, Buck's instinct tells him what he has to do.

- **mercy:** kindness

  In the wild, the dogs showed no mercy toward each other.

- **rivalry:** an intense competition

  Buck and another dog have a bitter rivalry over who will be the top dog.

Reader Tips Here's how to get the most out of this book.

- **Meet the Characters** Check out the characters on pages 6–7. Connect their names with their pictures as you read.

- **Setting** The setting is when and where a story takes place. This story is set in the Alaskan wilderness. The setting is very important in this story. Review the descriptions of the wilderness. Think about how the setting affects the characters and their actions.

Meet the Characters

This story takes place in Alaska about one hundred years ago.

The Dogs

Buck
A big, strong dog. He had a great life in California as a pet. But life is tough in Alaska. Now, he works for his food. And he hears the call of the wild.

Spitz
Buck's enemy on the dogsled team. Spitz teaches Buck what the dog-eat-dog world is like.

The People

Perrault and Francois
Mail carriers who travel by dogsled. Perrault and Francois wonder if Buck will be tough enough for the dogsled team.

Charles, Hal, and Mercedes
Prospectors looking for gold. Instead, they find trouble. They don't know much about the wilderness, and it shows.

John Thornton
A real mountain man. He knows the wilderness. He loves his dogs. And Buck will do anything for him.

1

Dog Snatchers

Buck learns the law of the club.

"Here, Buck! Good dog." Buck lifted his head from his paws. It was Manuel, the gardener. "Let's go for a walk."

Buck stretched. A walk would be nice. His claws clicked down the porch steps.

Buck lived with Judge Miller and his family on a farm in California. There was always plenty of food. On cool nights, he slept by a warm fire. It was a good life.

Manuel and Buck came to a dirt road. A man in a red sweater leaned against a truck.

"He *is* big," the man said. Then Buck heard him counting dollar bills.

"Sorry, boy," Manuel said. He tied a rope around Buck's thick neck. "My family needs the money."

Manuel handed the rope to the man in the red sweater. Buck was confused. Did the judge know what was going on? He snarled and leaped at the man's hand. The man jumped back and yanked the rope tight. Buck fell, choking. Then everything went dark.

Buck woke up many hours later. He was in a metal cage. Buck could smell other dogs. The steel door at the end of the room screeched open. The man in the red sweater came in. Buck sat up and growled.

The man walked straight to Buck's cage. "We've got a week till the ship reaches Alaska," he said, looking in. Buck's lips curled back to flash his sharp **fangs.** The man opened the cage door. "Time to break you."

Like a bull, Buck charged at the red sweater. Then something hit him under the chin. The pain was terrible. Buck yelped and fell back. Then he scrambled to his feet. Again he charged. Buck now saw the man had a club. It came down hard on Buck's neck. Buck crashed to the floor. Everything was foggy.

Buck backed away. Who was this man? Why was he beating him like this? Buck had never felt so much pain. But he couldn't control his rage. A dozen times he flew at the man. A dozen times the club slammed into him. Finally, Buck could not get up.

The man in the red sweater pulled out a knife. He cut off Buck's collar and read the tag. "Well, Buck, if you're good, I'll treat you right. If you're bad, I'll beat the stuffing out of you."

Finally, the man held out strips of red meat. Buck gulped them down.

"That's a boy. You'll make a fine sled dog for somebody," the man said.

---**Heads Up!**---

The man in the red sweater beats Buck cruelly. What is he trying to do to Buck?

Buck can't control his rage.

2

Torn to Pieces

Buck learns the law of the fang.

The man in the red sweater took Buck all the way up to Seattle, Washington. And that was the last Buck ever saw of him.

Now he was aboard a great ship. It was headed for Alaska. His new owner spoke with a strange accent. But he seemed fair enough.

Buck also made a friend. Curly was a good-natured Newfoundland who was also making the trip to Alaska. She licked Buck's nose the first time they met. They were almost never apart after that.

The trip to Alaska took a long time. When they finally got there, Buck snapped at the white bugs falling from the sky. But they weren't bugs.

"Ha! Never seen snow, my friend?" said the man with the funny accent. Then another man arrived with eight other dogs. Buck and Curly looked at each other. What was going on?

"Welcome to Skagway!" the man with the funny accent said to the dogs. "I am Perrault. This is Francois. And you, my friends, are going to pull our mail sled to Dawson."

Perrault picked up one of Buck's muddy paws and showed it to Francois.

"His feet are soft."

"They'll get tough soon enough," Francois replied. He carried a bag marked "Mail." He tossed it down with a grunt. Then the two men went into the building. Buck whined. But he stopped when a large white dog growled at him.

The dog's name was Spitz. Buck saw how the other dogs acted around Spitz. Their heads and tails were lowered. They were afraid of him.

Heads Up!

In 1897, gold was found in parts of Alaska. Thousands of people rushed there to try to get rich. People there needed dogs to pull sleds through the snow. And they would pay good money for big, strong dogs.

Buck shivered. But it wasn't because of the cold. This strange world seemed dangerous. There was no place dry or warm. He felt like something **wild** was sneaking up on him. And he didn't feel strong enough to face it. Curly, on the other hand, went over to a big husky to make friends.

There was no warning. Just a leap, the clashing sound of teeth, and a leap away. Buck turned around. He saw that Curly's face was ripped open from eye to jaw.

Buck was horrified. He had never seen the wolf way of fighting before. He didn't know what was to come. He didn't understand why dogs from everywhere ran over and surrounded Curly. They licked their chops and waited.

Curly rushed at her attacker. But another dog sprang and knocked Curly off her feet. Her squeal set off the circle of dogs. They closed in on her, snarling and yelping.

Francois ran out of the building with a club in his hand. He beat the dogs back. But he was too late. They had already torn Curly to pieces.

So this was his new life, Buck thought. He turned away. Spitz was watching him. His mouth was bloody. He seemed to be laughing at Buck. Buck hated him already.

Heads Up!

Buck had a comfortable life in California. How is his new life different?

3

Running With the Big Dogs

Pulling a sled is hard work. Can Buck keep up?

The next day, they went to work. They raced through the snow at top speed. Buck's **harness** cut into his neck. The other dogs had all pulled sleds before. But Buck often tripped on the ropes. When he did, Perrault's whip cut into his back.

"Six hundred miles to Dawson, my friends!" Perrault roared from the sled. "No time for **tenderfeet**!"

Finally, they stopped to rest. Buck dropped like a dead dog. His feet were bloody. Snow was packed between his toes. But he was too tired to lick it out.

By the end of the second day, Buck knew that "ho" meant stop. And he knew that "mush" meant go. Soon he could pull without getting tangled in the ropes.

Still, the work seemed endless. And seeing Spitz in the front harness hurt Buck's pride. The dog he hated was the team's leader.

Day after day, the dogs pulled the sled. And each day, Buck learned more about his new life. Buck learned to gulp his food so Spitz couldn't steal it. He learned to dig holes in the snow to hide from the wind at night. And he felt a change come over his body. His muscles became hard. His paws felt tough as leather.

Now he knew he could survive in this cruel land. It felt like a wolf was waking up inside his chest. But as Buck grew stronger, Spitz became more **aggressive.**

─Heads Up!─

How would you describe the relationship between Buck and Spitz?

Buck is growing stronger from all the hard work.

4

Fight to the Death

Buck and Spitz see who will be top dog.

If the dogs didn't do their duty, it was Spitz's job to punish them. All the dogs had felt Spitz's fangs on their throats.

All except Buck. Several times, Spitz had gone after him. But Buck never let Spitz beat him. He was too big and quick and proud.

Their **rivalry** grew as the team neared Dawson. One morning, a dog was slow to line up. Spitz went after him. Buck jumped between them. Spitz bared his fangs like white knives. But Buck showed no fear.

Finally, Perrault snapped his whip. He stopped the fight before it could begin. But Buck had challenged Spitz. And everyone knew it.

"Sooner or later Spitz will kill that Buck," Perrault told his partner.

"I wouldn't be so sure about that," Francois replied, half smiling.

After three weeks on the trail, the team reached Dawson. They delivered the mailbags. Then they set up camp near a creek.

One night, Buck surprised a rabbit. It ran for its life along the frozen creek. All the dogs took off after it. Except for Spitz.

Buck led the chase. He felt strong and alive, more alive than ever before. The rabbit and the dogs rounded a creek bend. There was Spitz, waiting. The rabbit screamed as the white dog pounced. All the dogs howled with a hunter's joy.

But Buck's **instincts** had taken over. He saw Spitz, but he didn't stop. Buck's whole body slammed right into Spitz. The two dogs tumbled through the snow. The fight to the death had finally come.

Heads Up!

Look up instinct *in the glossary. What does it mean to say that "Buck's instincts took over"?*

Spitz and Buck are going to fight to the death.

Spitz proved why he had won so many fights. Every time Buck went for his throat, Spitz blocked him. Then Spitz went on the attack. Soon, Buck was covered in blood.

Now Buck was limping. Spitz was sure Buck was hurt. Spitz circled. He had beaten his enemy. He was going to finish him off.

But before Spitz could spring for the kill, Buck chomped on Spitz's front left paw. The bone crunched. He caught Spitz's right leg. He crushed that one, too. Buck had only been pretending. He had tricked Spitz. And now Spitz was helpless. Buck showed no **mercy.** He charged and knocked Spitz onto his back. The other dogs closed in. Spitz's white fur disappeared under them.

Buck stood back. He lifted his head and howled like a wolf into the star-filled sky.

Heads Up!

Buck "howled like a wolf." What is happening to Buck? How is the setting affecting him?

Gold Diggers

**Buck's new owners are after gold.
Are they headed for trouble?**

With Spitz gone, Buck took over as leader of the dog team. And none of the dogs minded.

In a few days, Buck had the team pulling as if it were one powerful dog. The mail sled raced back from Dawson to Skagway. They were home in 14 days.

"It's a record!" Francois shouted. He hugged Buck's neck. "No one has ever made the trip so fast!" he said.

But the celebration didn't last long. Perrault came into camp one morning. "I have bad news," Perrault said to the dogs. "You wore yourselves out on that last trip. I'm afraid the government is making us sell you. They want fresh dogs."

That afternoon, the dogs met their new owners, Hal and Charles. Buck noticed something different about these men. They had no beards and they smelled strange. Like soap and flowers. One sniff made Buck sneeze.

But even though the men smelled clean, their camp was a mess. Their big, gray tent sagged. And their dirty dishes were in the mud.

"Hey, Mercedes!" Charles called. A dark-haired woman poked her head out of the tent. She was Charles' wife and Hal's sister. "Let's head to the Dawson gold fields and get rich!"

Buck watched as his new masters packed up their gear. They loaded way too much on the sled. Still, Hal strapped Buck and the other dogs into their harnesses.

Mercedes sat herself down on the sled. "I'll ride like a princess," she said with a smile.

Two **miners** came out of a nearby tent. They wore mud-caked jeans and smelled like wood smoke. "Looks like you're carrying a bit much, friends," one of the miners said. "And your dogs are worn out."

"They're just lazy," Hal said. "Mush!" He lifted his whip. The tip stung one of the dogs, and he yelped. Buck and the team pulled with all their strength. The sled didn't budge.

"You're new here, aren't you?" the other miner said. He was trying not to laugh.

Charles' cheeks turned red, but he didn't reply.

"You better throw off half that load," said the first miner. "And get rid of the tent. Spring's almost here."

Charles and Hal looked angry. But they moved to unpack the sled. They got rid of the tent and the dishes—and Mercedes' clothes. She sobbed as she climbed back on the sled.

Finally, the load was light enough. The two miners watched the sled move slowly. "We should wish them good luck," one said.

The other one spat. "Shame to waste good luck, though."

─Heads Up!─

Compare Hal and Charles to the two miners they talk to. Who has more experience? How can you tell?

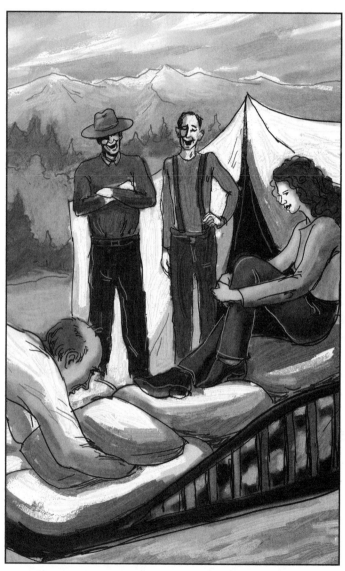

The miners laugh because the sled is too heavy to pull.

6

Hope Runs Out

Can anything save the dogs from starving to death?

"They said this was a great dog team. I think we got tricked." Hal stirred the smoky fire with a stick. "We're only halfway to the gold fields."

"Maybe we need to feed them a little more," Charles replied.

Mercedes looked away. For a while, she had been sneaking dried fish to the team. Now, most of the food was gone.

At first, Buck's pride kept him going. But without food, the team grew weaker. And Hal used his whip more and more.

They were on the same trail the mail sled had taken to Dawson. But now, Buck could feel the snow melting under his paws. Soft snow made the sled harder to pull.

One morning one of the dogs couldn't get up. He was too weak from hunger. Hal took out his pistol and shot the dog. The blast hurt Buck's ears. Soon, two more dogs died from hunger. Buck and the others kept the sled moving.

Days later, the team stumbled into a camp. It was near the mouth of the White River, three-quarters of the way to Dawson. A man in a green shirt sat alone on a rock. He was carving a thick stick with his knife.

"Ho!" Hal yelled. The dogs fell to the ground. They panted weakly.

The man glanced from Charles to Hal to Mercedes. He shook his head when he looked at the starving dogs.

"Only fools would ride on the ice now," he answered. "It's mighty thin."

"That's your opinion," Charles said. "We know what we're doing."

The man didn't say anything back.

Hal turned to the dogs. "Get up!" The whip cracked several times. Most of the dogs crawled to their feet. But not Buck. His hope was gone. He knew the ice was bad.

Hal swore. He pulled out his club. He struck Buck twice. "Get up, Buck!" he snarled.

Suddenly, the man in the green shirt was up. He lunged at Hal and caught his arm. "Hit that dog again and I'll whip you," he warned.

Hal broke away. He drew his long knife. The man swung his stick. It rapped Hal's knuckles and knocked the knife to the ground. The man picked it up. He cut Buck free.

Then the man petted Buck's bruised body. "I don't feel any busted bones, boy," he said. Minutes later, Hal drove the sled onto the river ice.

Suddenly, they heard Mercedes scream. Buck and the man looked up. A huge hole opened in the ice. People, dogs, and sled all fell through the hole. They dropped into the black water. They would not make it back out.

Buck licked the man's hand.

Heads Up!

What season is it now? How can you tell?

7

Man's Best Friend

Buck learns the law of love and kindness.

The man's name was John Thornton. He had been mining for gold with a partner. But Thornton's feet had frozen in the cold. They hurt so much that he couldn't walk. So he set up a camp and waited for his feet to heal. His partner, Hans, went to Dawson for help.

Buck stayed with Thornton. His camp was near the river bank. At night, Buck could hear wolves howling in the woods. Sometimes, he dreamed he was running with a **pack** of shadowy dogs. Once, he was sure he heard them calling to him.

But those were just dreams. Buck was happy with Thornton. The man talked to Buck all the time. He fed him from his own cooking pot. Slowly, he nursed the dog back to health.

One day, a bearded man came floating down the White River on a raft. He used a pole to push it to the bank near camp. Buck's barks boomed at the stranger.

"Hey, John!" the man called.

"Hans!" John replied. He put a hand on Buck's back to calm him down.

"Goodness, John. No one better touch you while that monster's around," Hans said, looking at Buck.

The two men loaded the raft. Then the men and Buck drifted down to Dawson. There Buck soon showed that Hans had been right.

The night they arrived, a man at the saloon was making fun of a boy. The boy happened to have big ears. The man thought they were funny. The boy was trying hard not to cry.

"There's no need to talk to the lad like that," Thornton said to the man.

Heads Up!

Where are Buck and John Thornton at the beginning of the chapter? How is the setting affecting Buck's dreams?

Without warning, the man turned and punched Thornton.

Buck had been napping in a corner. Thornton's fall woke him. Buck jumped up. He slammed into the man's chest. Buck left the bully bitten and bleeding on the floor.

A few days later, Thornton was chatting with some men at the same saloon. One miner bragged that his best dog could pull a 500-pound sled.

Thornton smiled. "My dog, Buck, can pull 1,000 pounds."

"Can he pull it for 100 yards?" the miner asked. Thornton nodded.

"I've got $1,000 that says he can't," the man said. He slammed a bag of gold dust onto the table. "And I happen to have a sled outside. It's got 1,000 pounds of flour on it."

Thornton swallowed hard. He didn't know if Buck could pull it. And he sure didn't have $1,000. He folded his arms. "I'll bet my dog, my sled, and all my gear against your bag of gold."

"It's a bet!" the miner said. People poured into the street to watch the contest.

Thornton hitched Buck to the sled. Buck could feel the crowd's excitement. He knew he had to do something special for Thornton.

"Give it your best, Buck," Thornton whispered. He held Buck's big head. Then he stood. "Mush!"

Buck backed up, then drove forward. The sled didn't move an inch.

"Mush!" Thornton yelled again.

Every muscle in Buck's body tightened. His claws scraped the snow. The sled shook, then jerked. Buck's love for Thornton made him try with all his might.

The sled inched forward. It stopped. Then it started again. It gained speed. The crowd gasped. When Buck passed the 100-yard mark, a huge cheer roared through Dawson.

Thornton threw his arms around the big dog's neck. Tears streamed down his cheeks. And Buck licked them away.

Heads Up!

Describe two ways in which Buck shows his love for Thornton.

Buck pulls a thousand pounds of flour while the crowd cheers.

8

Answering the Call

Will Buck stay with Thornton or run with the wolves?

Thornton paid his debts with the money Buck had won. Then he and Hans used the rest to go hunting for gold.

Sure enough, that summer the men found their treasure. They had hiked into a broad valley. It was far from any town. Gold **nuggets** glittered among the river rocks.

Buck pawed at a yellow rock. He barked until Hans looked over. Hans laughed. "We've got a gold-sniffing dog!"

Buck didn't understand their love of the yellow rocks. But his tail wagged when he saw how happy they made Thornton.

The men filled many bags with gold. Soon, the heavy bags stacked up.

Buck had little to do but nap, hunt, and explore. The pack of shadowy dogs came more often in his dreams now. But Buck did not want to leave Thornton.

One night, Buck snapped awake. He heard the same howl. But it was closer than ever before. It called to him. But this was no dream. He ran out of the camp. He ran to the sound.

In a moonlit clearing he saw it. It was a wolf. The wolf saw Buck and ran away. But Buck was faster. He cornered it against a rock.

Buck did not show his fangs or growl. The wolf finally understood that Buck wasn't hunting him.

The two beasts looked at each other. One was wild. The other came from the world of men. They carefully sniffed noses. Then they played together, racing between the trees.

Heads Up!

Dogs originally came from wolves. Humans took wolves in and bred them to be tame. Is Buck tame, wild, or both? Explain.

Then Buck remembered Thornton. He whined to the wolf. He felt like he belonged out here. But he turned and trotted back toward his master.

The sun was coming up. Buck neared the camp. He heard voices. But they didn't belong to Thornton or Hans.

On the trail Buck saw a body. It was Hans. He was lying face down, dead. Arrows stood up from his back.

Buck charged into camp with his fangs bared. Strange people were dancing there. They were Yeehat warriors. They stabbed at the ground with spears. This was their land. And they had killed the **trespassers.**

Buck tore into the Yeehat warriors like a storm. He ripped the throat out of one man, then two others. The others tried to stab the raging dog. But Buck was too fast. Finally, the warriors ran. Buck chased them along the river. He did not stop until he had dragged them all down.

Then Buck went back to camp. He sniffed for Thornton. He followed his master's tracks. They led to the water. Buck took two steps into the stream. He smelled blood. No tracks came out.

The moon rose as Buck lay near the stream. He knew Thornton was gone. An ache pounded in his broad chest. He was no longer a pet. Or a sled dog. Or Thornton's friend. What was he? Where did he belong?

Buck heard a short yelp. He looked to the trees. He saw his brother wolf, waiting. Ever since he had come to Alaska, the wildness had been growing inside Buck. Now his instincts told him what to do. He was ready to answer the call.

Buck walked toward the wolf. Together, they disappeared into the forest.

Heads Up!

Think about how Buck has changed since the beginning of the book. Do you think he'll be able to survive in the wild now? Why or why not?

Jack London

(1876–1916)

In 1876, Jack London was born into a poor family in San Francisco. At age ten, he fell in love with reading. But he left school when he was only 14 to help make money for his family.

Jack worked hard as a young man. He sold newspapers and took whatever job he could find. But he wanted more than anything to be a writer.

He also loved adventure. Jack worked as a sailor and hopped freight trains. He also searched for gold in Alaska, like the characters in *The Call of the Wild.* He loved the wilderness and sailing on the open sea.

London turned his adventures into stories. And he became one of the most popular writers of his day. *The Call of the Wild, Sea-Wolf,* and *White Fang* are three of his most famous novels.

He died from kidney disease when he was only 40 years old.

Glossary

aggressive *(adjective)* hostile in going after what you want (p. 17)

fang *(noun)* a long, sharp tooth (p. 9)

harness *(noun)* straps that connect an animal to something it's pulling (p. 16)

instinct *(noun)* a gut feeling about what to do in order to survive (p. 20)

mercy *(noun)* kindness (p. 22)

miner *(noun)* someone who digs or searches for valuable metals or minerals (p. 24)

nugget *(noun)* a small lump or piece of something, usually a valuable metal (p. 35)

pack *(noun)* a group of dogs or wolves (p. 30)

rivalry *(noun)* an intense competition (p. 19)

tenderfoot *(noun)* someone who is new at something and needs practice (p. 16)

trespasser *(noun)* someone who enters someone else's property without permission (p. 37)

wild *(adjective)* not tamed, not controlled (p. 14)